Invent an Insect

by Judith Brand
illustrated by Rick Stromoski

Harcourt

Orlando   Boston   Dallas   Chicago   San Diego

Visit *The Learning Site!*

www.harcourtschool.com

"Many little animals are insects," Chip says. "Some fly and some don't."

"Come on," says Bess. "We'll watch some insects to see what they are like."

Mitch watches insects from the bench. Chip watches insects going up a branch.

4

Bess turns to watch a butterfly.
You can watch insects where
you live!

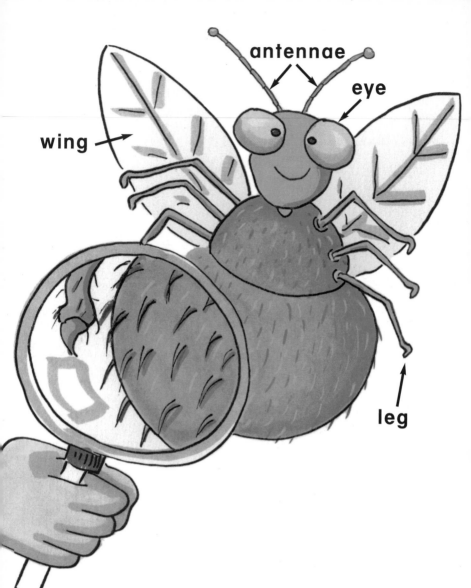

antennae

eye

wing

leg

Insects have six legs. They have two matching antennae. Some have wings.

6

Mitch, Bess, and Chip chat on the bench. "Let's invent new insects," says Mitch.
You can invent one, too!

Mitch, Bess, and Chip soon
sketch their insects. You can
sketch one, too!

8

Bess says, "My insect will fly
around in the air. You can't catch
it. It's much too fast. It's a flying
champ!"

"My insect's very big," Chip says.
"It's as long as my body!"

"My insect BIT me!" Mitch says.
"It bit my chin. It itches so much."

11

Now it's YOUR turn! Invent your insect.